Nurse Ted
A Children's Guide to Cancer

Ffion Jones ● **Kerry Foster-Mitchell**

With thanks to the Fountain Centre, the Royal Surrey County Hospital, and all our supporters.

To John Wynne; with love,

and in memory of Marcello, Siewli, and Lucy; always remembered.

www.nurseted.com

First Published 2016 by Belrose Books. Copyright © 2016 Nurse Ted Ltd in accordance

with the Copyright, Designs and Patents Act, 1988.

"Nurse Ted" story text and illustrations by Ffion Jones. www.ffijones.com

The moral rights of Ffion Jones to be identified as author and illustrator of the "Nurse Ted"

story have been asserted.

Glossary, Parent's/Carer's Guide, Questions and Answers page (text), Side Effects page by

Kerry Foster-Mitchell. Her moral rights have been asserted.

ISBN 978-0-9931579-4-3

I 'm Nurse Ted and I work here at the hospital.

I like working here because I like helping people to get better when they are sick.

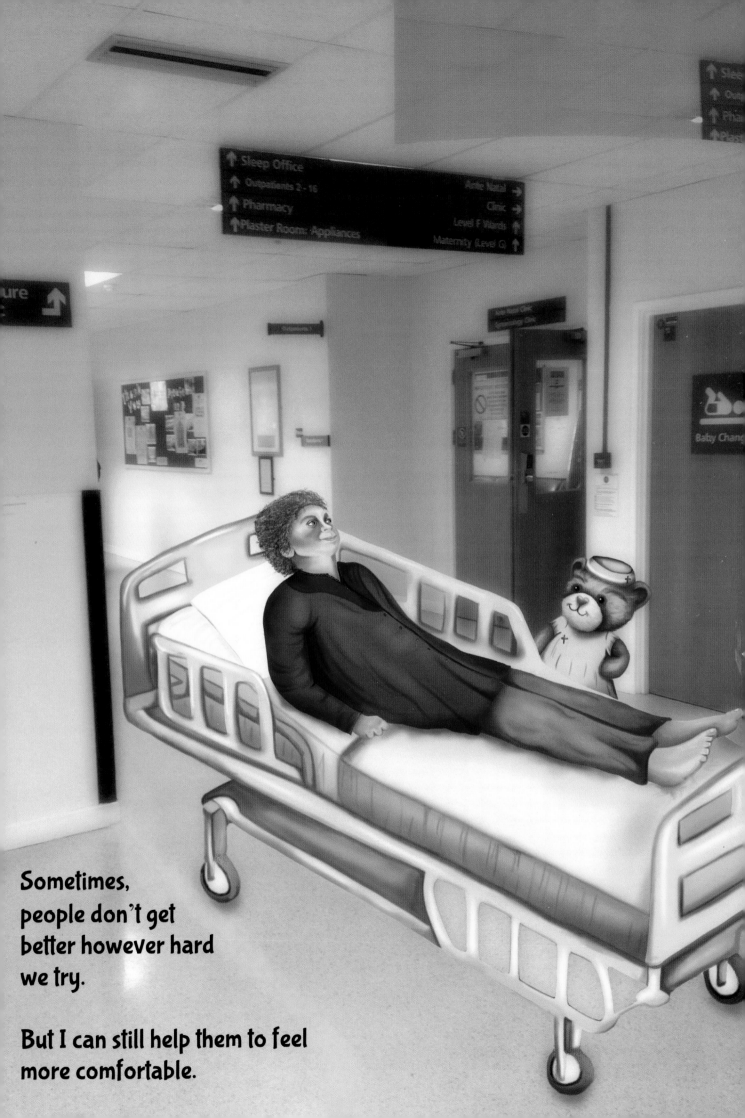

Sometimes,
people don't get
better however hard
we try.

But I can still help them to feel
more comfortable.

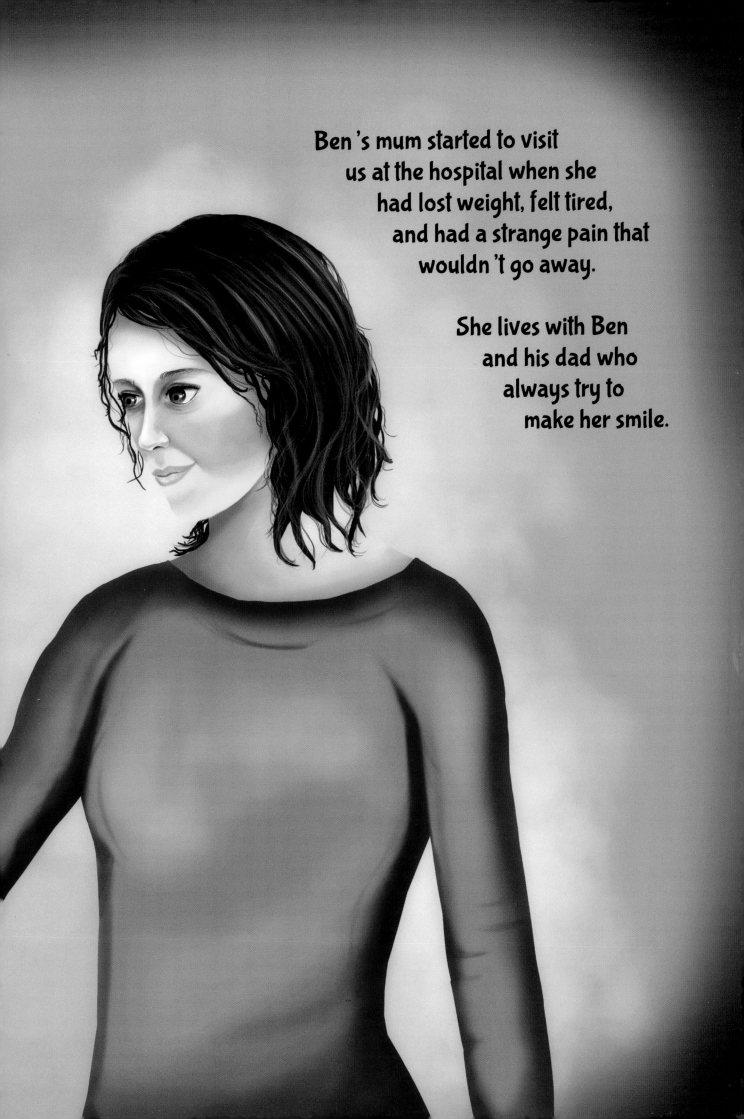

Ben's mum started to visit
us at the hospital when she
had lost weight, felt tired,
and had a strange pain that
wouldn't go away.

She lives with Ben
and his dad who
always try to
make her smile.

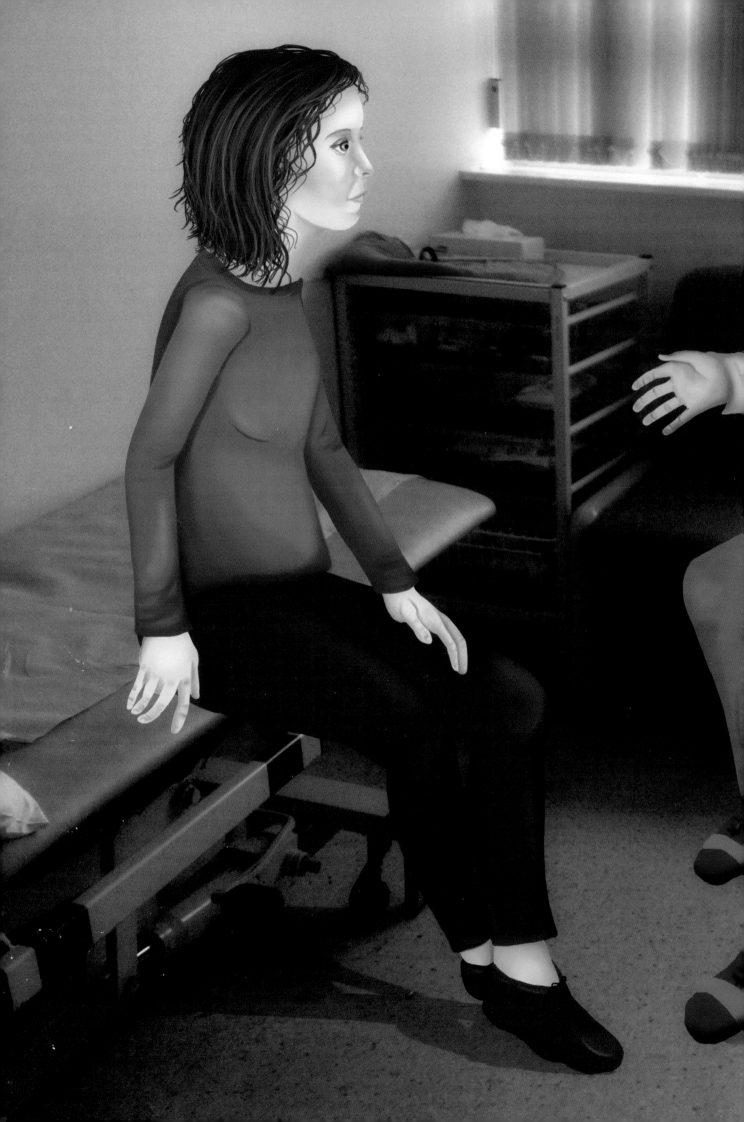

She went to see her doctor first who checked her and told her to rest for a while. He asked her to come back if she felt any worse.

Ben's mum rested but didn't feel any better. The doctor said her body may not be working properly and sent her to see us at the hospital.

We have special tests and machines to help us find out what is wrong with people's bodies.

Ben's mum had one of these tests called a scan. She had to stay very still when she was having the scan.

It took pictures, like a camera, of the inside of her body.

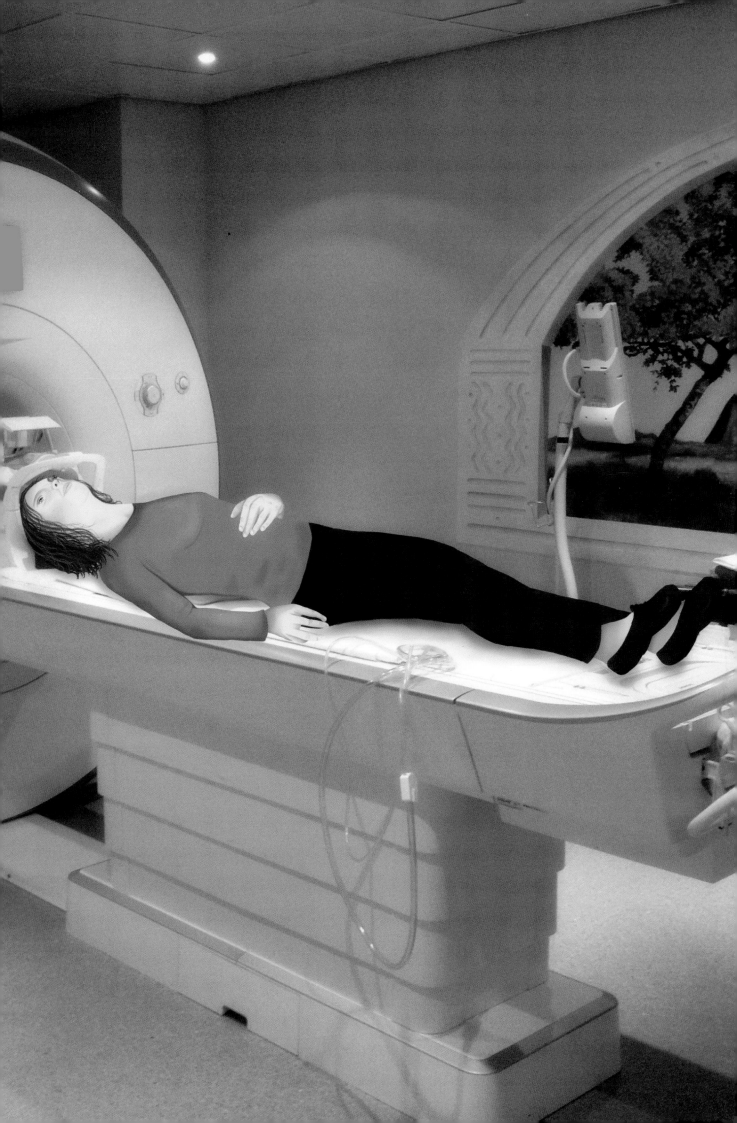

We looked at the pictures and saw a lump that was causing her sickness.

The lump is called a tumour.

Some tumours are not cancer.

But, after some more tests, we found that Ben's mum's tumour was a type of cancer.

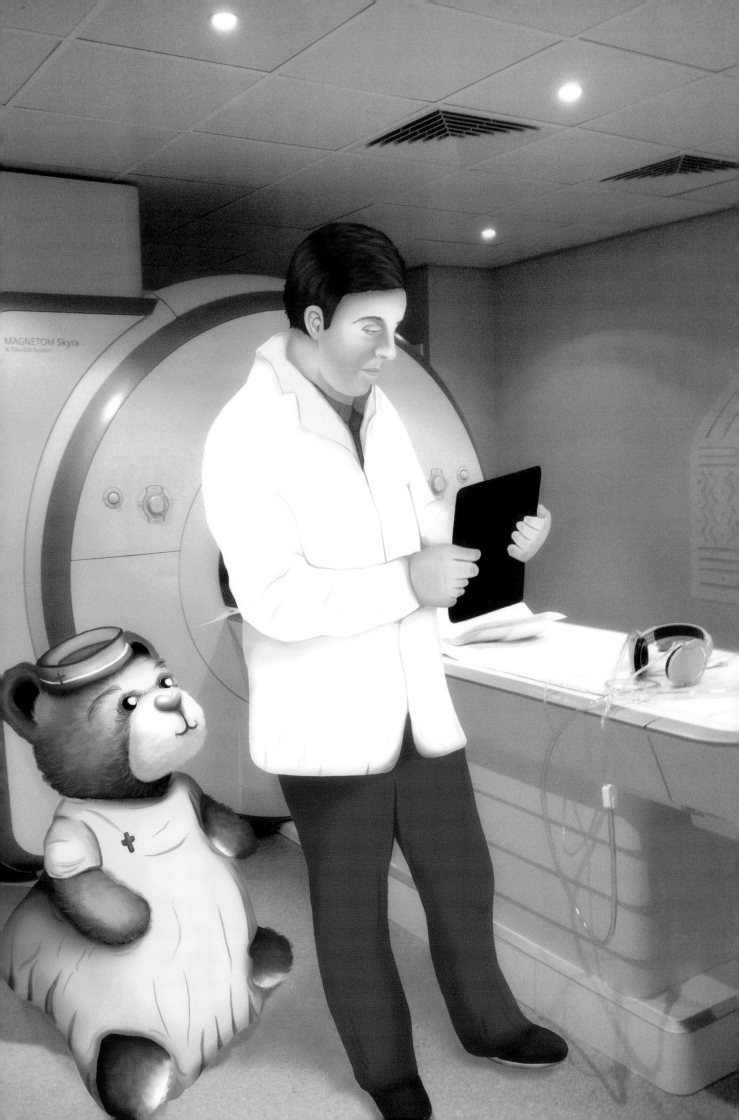

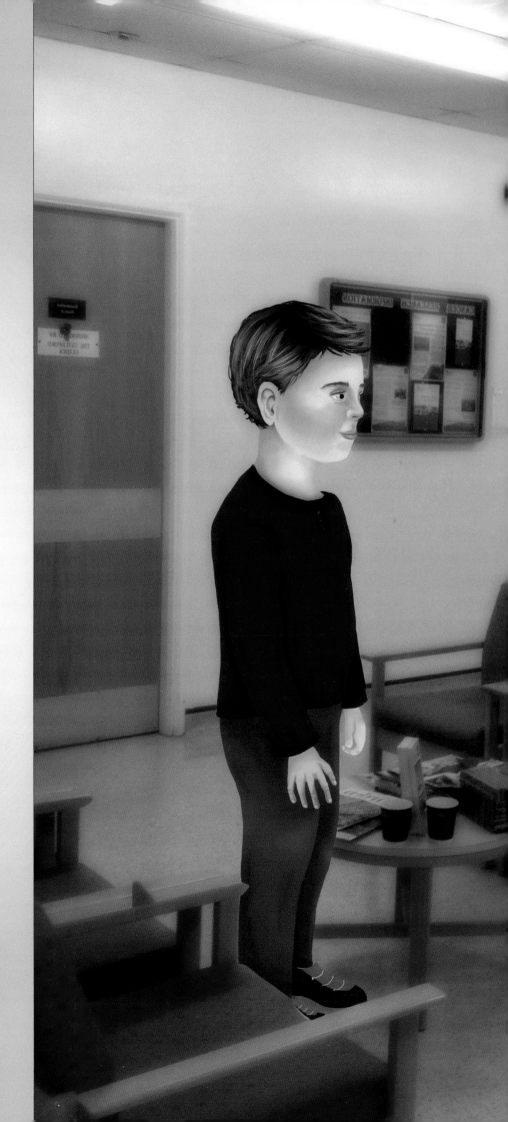

"What's cancer?" Ben asked because he felt a little scared.

"You'll feel less scared," I told him, "once I've explained it all to you."

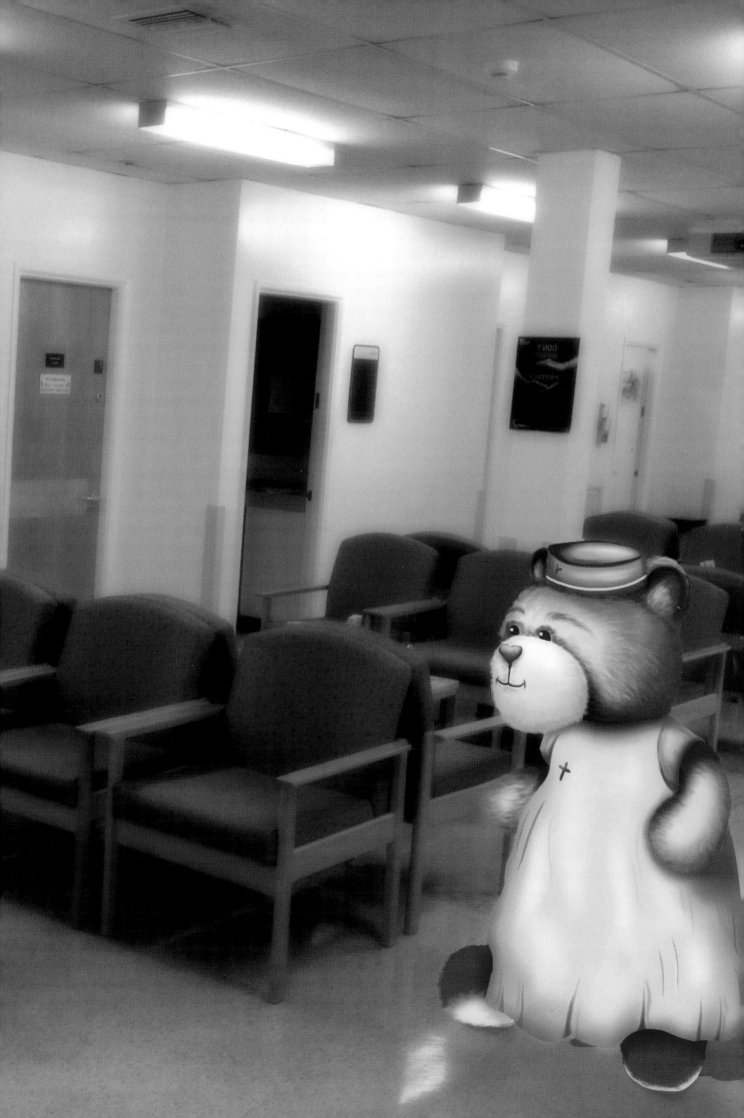

"Everyone is made up of trillions of tiny things called cells," I said, "which all have a special job to do to make your body work properly. But sometimes cells can get sick, just like we can."

"We don't always know why and it's nobody's fault; sometimes cells just grow when they shouldn't."

"The sick cells can join up to make a lump, called a tumour. The tumour can stop the healthy cells from working properly. This can make the person very sick."

"Now we have found your mummy's tumour," I explained, "the doctor will take some of it out so that he can look at it under a microscope to see what type of cancer it is."

I told Ben that every cancer
is different.

"Cancer is an umbrella
term for more than
100 different
illnesses where
cells grow
when they
shouldn't.

The sick
cells can
grow in different
parts of the body.

Sometimes, the sick cells stay in one
place and sometimes, they spread to
another part of the body.

Once we know more about your mummy's
tumour, we can try to help her in three different
ways: an operation, radiotherapy, and chemotherapy.
Sometimes, the sick cells can be quite strong so we
try to get rid of them in more than one way."

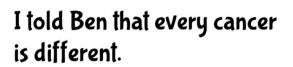

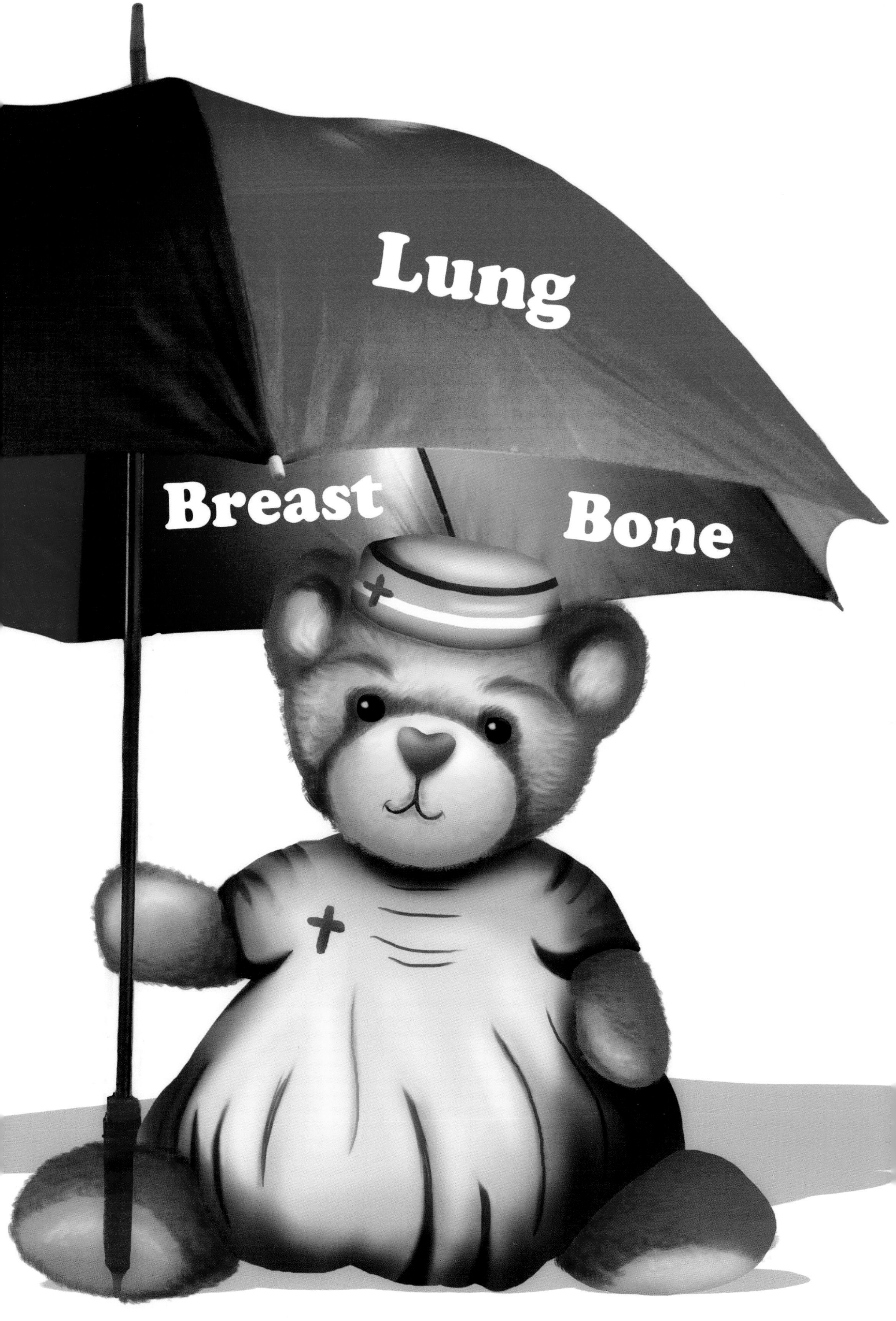
Lung
Breast
Bone

Ben was a little happier that we could try to help his mum and he asked,

"Can you tell me about the three different ways."

"It's good to ask questions," I said, "because talking through what may happen can make you feel less scared."

"First of all," I explained, "your mummy may have an operation to try to take some of the tumour out."

"She would have to stay in hospital for a while, but when she is here we would help her to feel better."

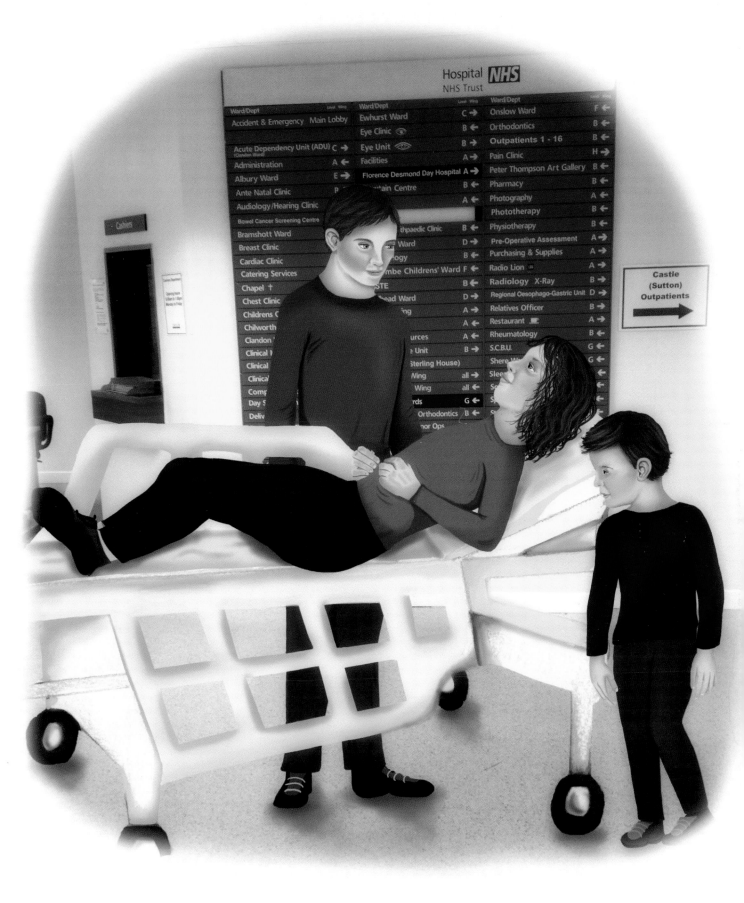

The doctors decided that Ben's mummy should have the operation. Ben was sad the first time his mum stayed with us at the hospital because he missed her and their cuddles.

But he knew that she was in the best place.

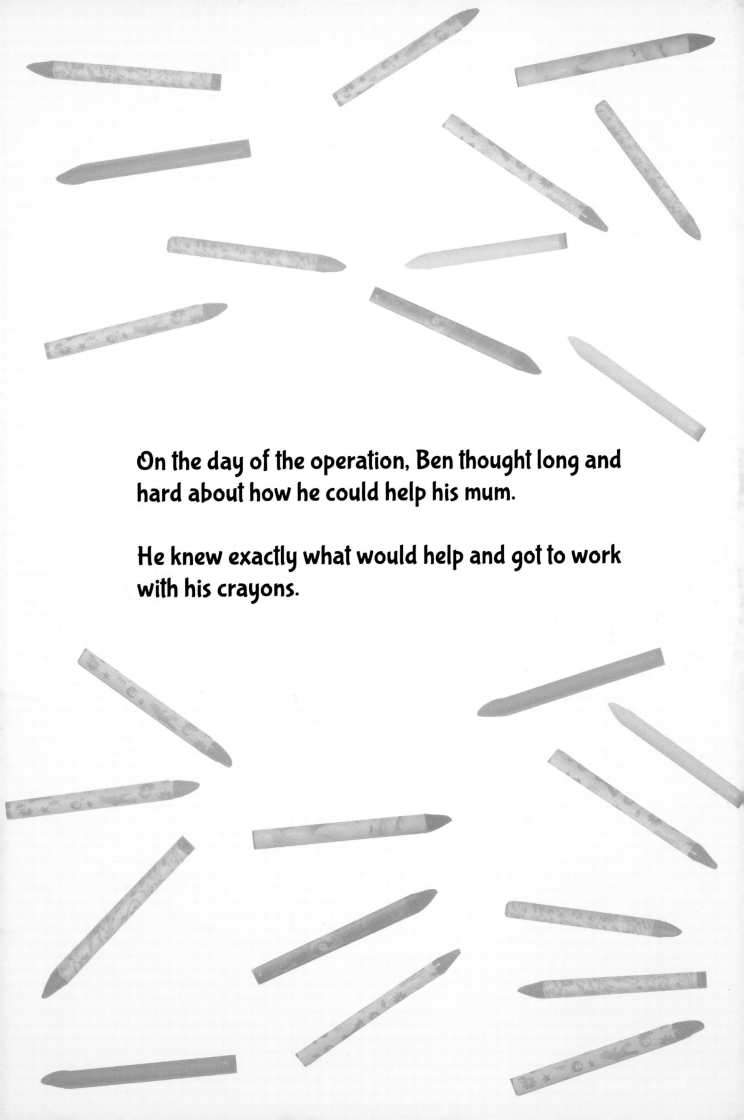

On the day of the operation, Ben thought long and hard about how he could help his mum.

He knew exactly what would help and got to work with his crayons.

When she woke up from the operation, Ben's mum
was tired and a little sore.

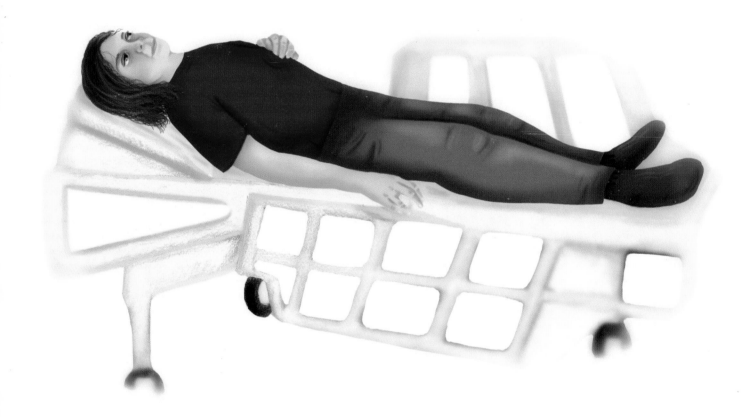

She stayed in a special ward called "Intensive Care"
so that the nurses could keep an eye on her and give her
medicine to make her feel better.

Soon she was back on another ward and Ben came
to visit with the biggest "Get Better Soon" card
I have ever seen.

The card put a big smile on his mum's face, which made
Ben smile too.

After some days in hospital, Ben's mum went home to rest for a while.

But Ben told his dad that he still felt sad.

"I'm happy mummy's home again but everything seems different now. I want things to go back to how they were before mummy got sick," he whispered.

Ben's dad explained that his mum was tired and weak because her body was fighting cancer.

"She may feel sick and spend a lot of time resting," he said, "but there is one special thing that will always stay the same. Your mummy will always love you and that will never change."

As Ben cried, his dad cuddled him closely and said it was ok to cry because it was ok to be sad.

"It's ok to be angry too," he whispered, "because we both love mummy."

And he told Ben that talking to each other would help because he wasn't on his own.

Ben already felt much better.

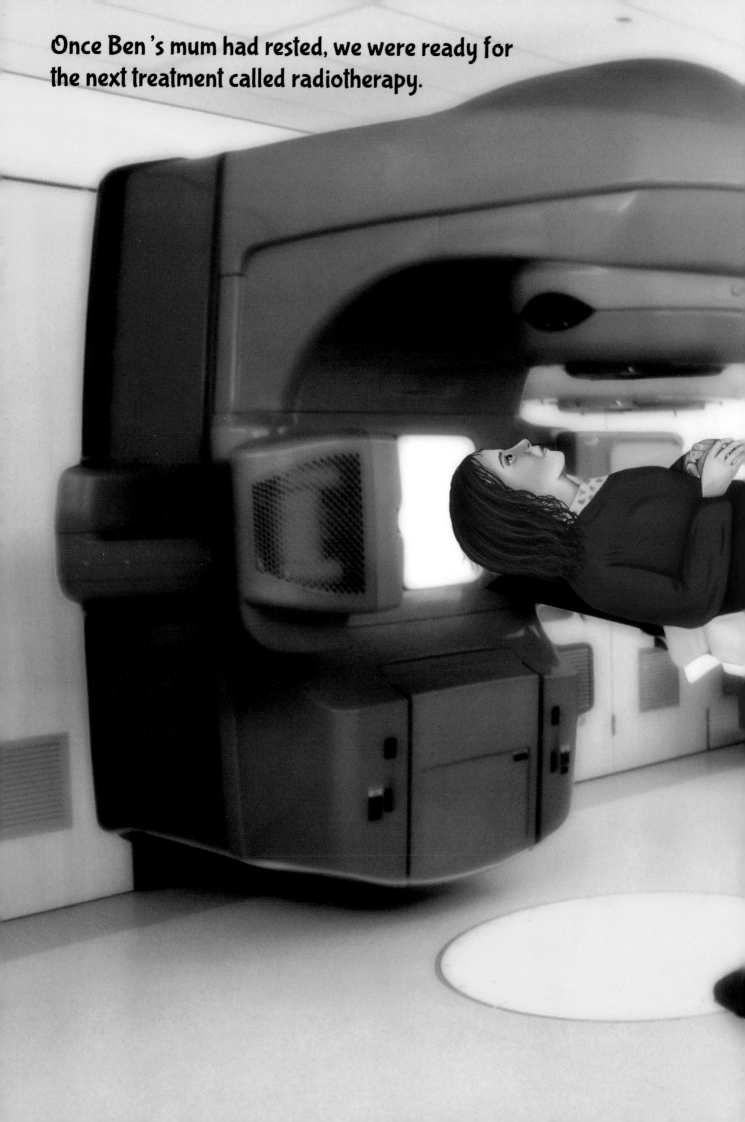

Once Ben's mum had rested, we were ready for
the next treatment called radiotherapy.

"Radiotherapy is like another scan," I explained, "to try to get rid of any sick cells left behind."

"Your mummy will lie down under a radiotherapy machine which will give her the medicine through invisible rays, like sun rays."

"We have to make sure that the rays only hit the sick cells, not the healthy ones."

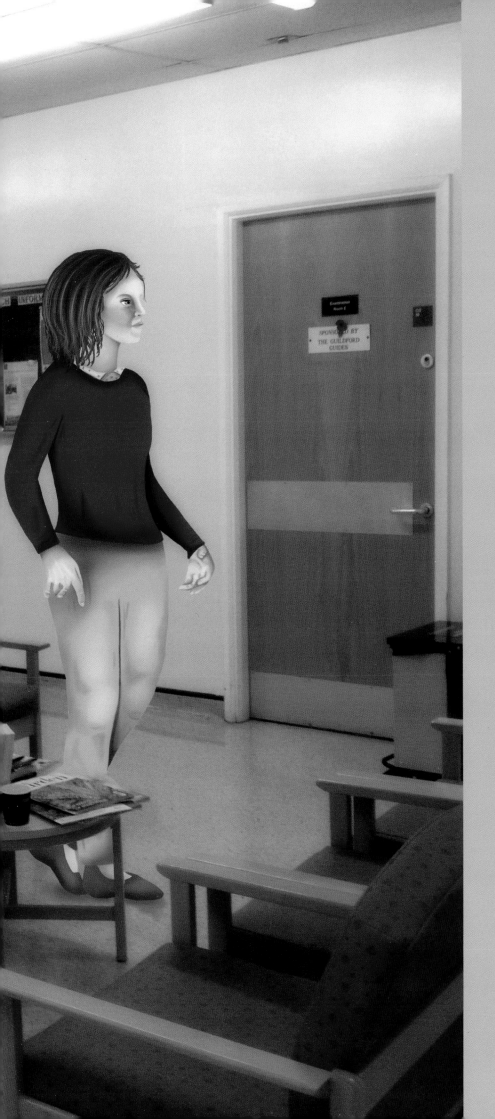

Ben's mum came to visit us every day for her radiotherapy sessions.

The sessions didn't hurt but made her feel tired.

"Don't worry," I told Ben, "she's tired because the medicine is working hard to try to get rid of the sick cells. The tiredness will get better after the treatment has finished."

Ben's mum also had the third type of treatment.

This was a medicine called chemotherapy to help get rid of the sick cells.

"The sick cells multiply too quickly," I explained, "so that one cell becomes two cells and then two cells become three cells and so on."

"The chemotherapy gets rid of these cells. The trouble is chemotherapy also gets rid of healthy cells that are meant to multiply quickly, like the cells that make your hair grow and white blood cells that help your body fight bugs like colds."

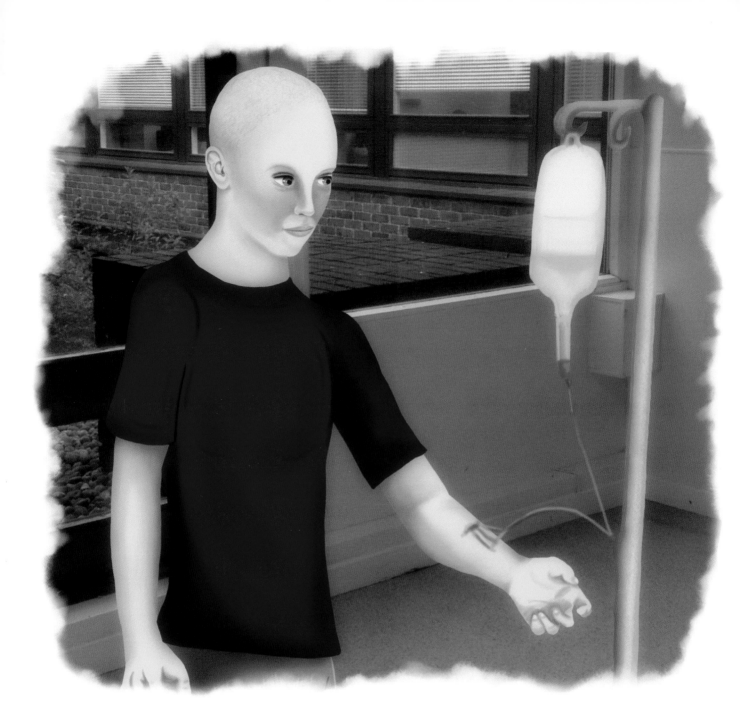

When Ben's mum had a high temperature, she had to stay in hospital so we could give her some special medicine. She had a room on her own to stop her catching any more bugs.

The chemotherapy also made her feel very ill but that was because it was helping her body to get rid of the sick cells.

Her hair started to fall out too, which showed that the chemotherapy was doing its job.

Ben was sad when his mum started to lose her hair, but he enjoyed helping her to choose a bright new scarf to wear.

Ben's mum has now started to feel much better.

Now that she has had the three treatments, she can stay at home with Ben and his dad and enjoy every moment together.

ENTRANCE

She still comes to visit us at the hospital every once in a while to make sure she is feeling ok.

And, sometimes, Ben likes to come with her.

After lots of practice at home,
Ben gives the best bear hugs a ted could ever want.

And his mum often tells me that,
whatever lies ahead,
those special hugs are the best medicine
she could wish for.

The End

Glossary

Benign – A tumour that is not cancer.

Biopsy – A test to collect a sample of cells and look at it under a microscope to help make a diagnosis.

Blood test – A sample of blood that is taken from a vein and looked at in a laboratory.

Cancer – A sickness caused by cells multiplying too quickly.

Cells – The building blocks of life. Human beings are made up of trillions of cells that help our bodies to work properly.

Chemotherapy – Special medicines used to treat cancer. They can be given as a tablet or by Intravenous Therapy (IV).

CT scan – A special scan which takes pictures of the inside of the body.

Diagnosis – The identification of an illness.

Infection – A germ inside someone's body which often causes a high temperature and makes the person feel unwell. The doctor may prescribe antibiotics to get rid of the germ.

Intravenous Therapy (IV) – A bag of liquid or medicines given into the vein.

Malignant – A tumour that is cancer.

MRI scan – A special scan which makes detailed pictures of the inside of the body.

Oncologist – A doctor who treats people with cancer.

Oncology clinic – A place where people with cancer are seen by the doctor and nurse.

Oncology Clinical Nurse Specialist – A nurse who looks after people affected by cancer.

Patient – A person who is being looked after by a doctor or nurse.

Radiotherapy – A special cancer treatment using x–rays. The x–rays are directed at cancer cells to try to stop them growing.

Radiotherapy Radiographer – A specially trained person who gives the x–ray treatment.

Scan – A picture of a part of your body. There are lots of different types of scans that a patient can have.

Steroids – Special medicines to help get rid of cancer cells and reduce swelling and to make chemotherapy work better.

Tests – A way to try to find out why someone is ill. For example, this could be a blood test or a scan.

Treatment – Medical care to help someone when they are ill. For example, antibiotics for an infection.

Tumour – A growth in the body which can be benign (not cancer) or malignant (cancer).

Side Effects of Treatment

Many of the treatments for cancer can cause side effects. But it is important to remember that treatment is there to help and is doing a lot of good.

Radiotherapy is a special cancer treatment using x-rays. The x-rays are directed at cancer cells to try to stop them growing.

Side effects may include:

- Hair loss in the treatment area. Hair in other parts of the body is not affected. The hair should grow back a few months after treatment.
- Sore/ red skin (like sunburn).
- Tiredness and weakness: both during the radiotherapy and for a while afterwards.
- Feeling sick. The doctor can give medicine to help.

Chemotherapy is a special medicine used to treat cancer. It can be given as a tablet or into a vein (intravenous therapy).

The main side effect is that it can reduce the number of blood cells in the body:

- White blood cells fight infection. If the patient gets a sore throat or fever or catches a cold, they must go straight to hospital. They may need antibiotics.
- Red blood cells carry oxygen around the body. Low levels may make the patient feel tired and dizzy.
- Platelets help stop bleeding. Low levels may make the patient bruise easily or have nosebleeds and bleeding gums.
- A blood test is done before chemotherapy to check blood levels.

Questions you may have when a family member has cancer.

- Cancer is a sickness caused by cells growing when they shouldn't.

- You can't catch cancer and we don't always know why people get cancer.

- It is nobody's fault; sometimes cells just get sick.

- Some people who have cancer do die and some people get better.

- With the help of the doctors and nurses, everything that can be done to treat the cancer is being done.

- The best thing you can do to help is to give your parents a big cuddle and lots of love.

Thoughts and Feelings

You can use these pages to jot down your thoughts and feelings or to draw a picture of your experiences.

Thoughts and Feelings

Parent's/Carer's Cut Out Guide

This book was created to help parents/carers who have cancer explain their diagnosis and treatment to their children. Books can help children to understand new situations and to visualise what is happening to their family member.

What to tell my children?

Talking about cancer is not an easy task, but sharing information early on can help to build trust with your children. Keeping them informed may help to make the situation less frightening.

Parents/carers who are open with their children from the start will often find that these children are less anxious. Being open with your children doesn't mean you have to tell them everything; what they need to know depends on their age. If you are unsure of what to say, talk to your doctor or nurse.

- Choose a quiet time when the house is calm. It is often best to tell your children at the same time but if there is a big age gap between them, you may want to tell the older siblings first. Children can be an amazing support to one another.

- Use age appropriate language that is easy to understand. Younger children, in particular, may want the information in small chunks. Don't worry if you don't finish the conversation as you can always revisit it another time. It is an ongoing process.

- Tell your children that it is OK to get upset and that crying is not a sign of weakness; it is an expression of our feelings. Encourage them to talk about how they are feeling and not to bottle things up as this may cause more distress.

- Ask the children if they have heard the words "cancer," "tumour," "surgery," "radiotherapy" and "chemotherapy." If they have heard these words, ask them what they understand by them. This can help to correct any misinformation that they may have picked up in the past.

© 2016 Nurse Ted Ltd

How to support my children through my treatment?

- Ask your children if they have any questions. You may not know the answers and it is OK to tell your children that you don't know. Tell them that you will do your best to help them find answers. It is also important to explain that the doctors don't always have the answers to questions either.

- Give the children permission to ask questions at any time. One suggestion is to make a thoughts, feelings and questions "post box." Leave it in an accessible location. Children can write down their thoughts, feelings and questions and leave them in the post box for later discussion. Having frequent conversations and family update meetings with your children can help them to feel heard, included, safe and secure.

- Ask your children if they want to visit the hospital and meet the doctors and nurses where you are being treated. It can be less scary for them if they know where you are going each day and who is looking after you.

- Spend time with your children having fun and doing normal daily activities. The routine of school and everyday activities help children to feel safe and secure. Try to keep children informed about any changes to their daily routine. You may need extra help from friends and family when you are having treatment. There will be many hospital appointments and times when you are feeling tired. You may have side effects from the treatment that make you feel unwell. Don't be afraid to accept help from friends and family.

- If your children are at school, tell the school about the changes at home. Schools can help to support children and often pick up any changes in behaviour.

- There are many different support services and healthcare professionals that want to help families just like yours. For example, in the South East area, Jigsaw South East (www.jigsawsoutheast.org.uk) works in partnership with Macmillan to support children, young people and their families that are affected by a family member who has a life limiting cancer. Also in the South East, the Fountain Centre (www.fountaincentre.org) supports cancer patients, their families and carers in the Royal Surrey County Hospital, Guildford, by offering advice, counselling and complementary therapies. There are similar centres around the UK. Speak to your healthcare team who can point you in the right direction.